Images from Nature

The Natural History Museum wishes to express its thanks and appreciation to Mr and Mrs John Duggan for their generous support in the production of this book and for their continued involvement in the Museum's work.

Images from Nature

Drawings and Paintings from the
Library of The Natural History Museum

The Natural History Museum would like to
thank Christies for exhibiting the artwork in this
book in February 1998 at their Ryder Street Rooms.

Applications for reproduction
should be addressed to:
Publishing Division
The Natural History Museum
Cromwell Road
London SW7 5BD

A catalogue record for this book is
available from the British Library

ISBN 0 565 09029 1

Designed by David Robinson
Colour reproduction and printing
by Craft Print Pte Ltd, Singapore

CONTENTS

FOREWORD

William Blake perceived 'a world in a grain of sand' and 'a heaven in a wild flower' – giving poetic shape to the artist's perception of the infinite wonder of the natural world. In every medium, artists have frequently drawn their inspiration from nature.

This book reproduces some of the works of art from the collection of The Natural History Museum which are both aesthetically pleasing and of scientific relevance. The portrayal – often in exquisite detail – of zoological and botanical specimens, captures the imagination bringing to artistic life a plant or animal described.

The collection was established to provide a scholarly stock of depictions of the natural world, but there is equal merit in the collection for the discerning lover of art. The items for inclusion in this book are a tantalising sample of the whole. Those who have no grasp of the science that is illustrated will enjoy the quality of the creative process, in the artist illuminating the natural world, the perception of the universal in the smallest element, the heavenly in every particle of nature.

Through the pages of *Images from Nature* you are invited to share in some of the treasures to be found in the manuscript, art and literature collections of The Natural History Museum.

Lord Palumbo

INTRODUCTION

There are many facets to The Natural History Museum. For many, particularly the young, The Natural History Museum is synonymous with dinosaurs. Older people, recalling their first visit some years ago, may still think of it as a treasure house of stuffed animals that they came to wonder at, before television made exotic creatures more familiar to us all. Others will immediately picture the building. Designed by Alfred Waterhouse in the last century it is one of the most distinctive and aesthetically pleasing buildings. Often described as a cathedral to nature, its rich decoration and vaulted construction bears comparison with the finest cathedrals. The museum professional is likely to have in mind the innovative exhibitions that help the visitor to interpret the wonders of the natural world.

The scientist will know the Museum as one of the premier centres for the study of taxonomy and research, aimed at helping us to better understand and preserve the diversity of life on our planet for future generations. The ordinary visitor is usually surprised to learn that behind the public galleries many scientists are at work. As well as the Museum's own staff, thousands of researchers from around the world come every year to work with the 68,000,000 specimens in the collections and consult the literature in the Library. It comes as an even greater surprise that the Museum is also home to one of the country's largest collections of art.

The Natural History Museum Library holds nearly a half million works of art on paper, made up of original drawings, watercolour paintings and prints. There is also a modest collection of oil paintings. Within its manuscript collections are many sketch-books and notebooks, sheets and letters which also contain delightful, curious or outstanding illustrations. In addition, among its one million books and twenty-five thousand journal titles are many unique or rare, lavishly illustrated volumes. They are all vital tools for the Museum's scientists and their taxonomic work. We need to consider some historical aspects of scientific collecting and the way new species are named and described to fully understand why this is so.

The eighteenth and nineteenth centuries in Europe saw an unprecedented growth of interest in the natural world. This interest was fed by the information and materials brought back from the many great expeditions and voyages that took place at the time and which opened up the continents and discovered new lands. Large numbers of animals and plants came to the attention of explorers and naturalists for the first time and their sponsors back in Europe wanted information about them. Prior to the development of rapid transport, sophisticated methods of moving living or preserving specimens and the invention of photography, the only way information about new animals and plants reached Europe, and was then disseminated, was by word of mouth, text or drawing. The latter method has distinct advantages when trying to fully convey the wonders of an animal like a kangaroo (p.51) to an audience who would have doubted such a creature, so different from anything known in Europe, could exist. Similarly, whilst text can describe the structure, colour and intricacies of, for example, the peony, only a few can command language so expertly that they can bring a flower to life as evocatively as the picture seen here by Bauer (p.71).

Whilst some well-preserved specimens and indeed live specimens were safely brought back, the long sea journeys and the agents of decay, frequently meant that specimens were of little value by the end of the voyage. Pictures on paper often fared better in the attempts to preserve them. Even the specimens that were safely brought back have often since perished whilst the drawings made of them have survived.

Unlike many scientific disciplines where information can rapidly become outdated information relating to natural history never dates. Once a description of a species has been published, anyone doing further work on that species or trying to determine if a specimen is of the same or a different species will refer back to the original description. Even if new information causes the species name to be modified or changed, the original description will still be referred to. The specimen from which the description was compiled is then known as the type specimen. Sadly many type specimens have not survived but often drawings of them have. In this case the latter are known as iconotypes and effectively take the place of the lost type specimen. The Natural History Museum collections include many drawings that come into this category.

That the collection has grown to be so large is due to several reasons. As explained above there is a practical need for representations of specimens in the day-to-day work of the staff of the Museum. Artists have been employed by the Museum to make drawings whilst many scientists have prepared their own drawings. These account for only part of the reason why the collection has grown to the size it has. The Museum has been fortunate that through gift or purchase it has managed to secure a number of large, major collections. Some of these were from the great voyages and expeditions of the past. For example, a substantial number of the specimens and drawings from Cook's three voyages are now housed in the collection including the work of the artist on the first voyage, Sydney Parkinson (pp.98–101). Many private collections have also been purchased, bequeathed or donated to the Library.

The Museum was also very active in the last two decades of the nineteenth century and early part of this century in acquiring rare books and original drawings. One of the principal reasons for this was that when the Museum moved to South Kensington from Bloomsbury most of the natural history books and drawings remained behind. It was not practical for the curators and researchers to keep travelling across London between the two buildings and the government made money available to establish the necessary collections. This coincided with a time when many great landed families were being forced, due to the prevailing economic situation, to sell their collections.

Although many of the problems associated with moving and preserving specimens have largely been overcome, and photography makes recording quick, there are numerous circumstances when for scientific purposes a drawing is far better than a photograph. A drawing allows details to be shown that cannot otherwise be revealed. The drawings by Church (pp.8-17), Bone (pp.34-35) and Terzi (pp.52-55) amply demonstrate the truth of this.

Additional to its scientific use the collection is also widely consulted by historians of both art and science. The earliest rare books date from the fifteenth century whilst the works of art range from the seventeenth century through to the present. This long time span, coupled with the fact that the work of all the great natural history artists is represented, makes it an invaluable reference collection for comparative purposes. The value is further enhanced by the other materials held. For many of the great figures in natural science the Museum not only holds their works of art but also their notebooks, diaries, letters, preliminary sketches and the published volumes. It is therefore possible to study many individuals in a truly holistic manner. The notebooks by Bates (pp.66-67), Ehret (pp.56-61) and Finch-Davies (pp.18-19) demonstrate this.

In selecting the images for display it was intended to try and fulfil several aims. Principal amongst these was to present a selection of items that reveal the range and diversity of subjects in the Museum's art collections. Natural history art is far more than just cuddly animals and pretty flowers. Few would intuitively expect that a horsefly, diminutive lichen or an ordinary pebble from the beach are subjects from which an arresting painting would result. The drawings by Terzi (pp.52-55), Dalby (pp.30-31) and Fullwood (pp.32-33) demonstrate how wrong such an assumption would be. The scale and detail the artists have captured in these works draws one in and compels admiration not only for the power of their observation but also for the way in which they have translated this onto the paper.

To avoid disappointing those who like the cuddly and pretty, this selection does include items that could be described as falling into these categories. There is, however, a great deal more to them than just these 'defining' characteristics. There are few animals more calculated to excite the human's 'cute' response than the koala, but has any other artist achieved what Ferdinand Bauer (pp.62-65) has in so accurately reproducing the animal's form or colour, lustre and texture of the fur? I have often noticed those looking at these drawings involuntarily move to put out a hand to test that it is not actually fur. Similarly, the flowers painted by his brother Franz (pp.68-73) exhibit a perfection that makes you wonder whether if you should return to see it tomorrow it would not be showing signs of wilting.

These images also demonstrate how artists have chosen to use a variety of techniques and media to convey the essential character and specific features of a particular specimen. The way in which the artist achieves this can often influence the way in which we look at animals and plants. Who, after looking at Kneale's drawing of a tortoise (pp.88-89), could not but have a heightened respect for this humble creature and look upon it with renewed respect for its strength, the beauty of its skeleton and the sense of age and wisdom conveyed by its head. But, how different in style from both of the Bauers or William MacGillivray (pp.104-111), Hargreaves (pp.36-41) or West (pp.102-103). Conversely, there is for me a great affinity between Kneale's work and the Waterhouse drawings (pp.74-81) for the Museum and the finished building. Kneale's bone drawing – the specimen stripped of all its exterior finery – recalls the solidity, yet fine detail of the cathedral to nature and the appropriateness of the structure to its purpose.

Different again is the approach of William Bartram (pp.26-29). His writings in his Travels (1791) reveal him to be truly a philosopher of the natural world. In his drawings he imparts both the humour and essence of his philosophy. At first glance his work appears straightforward. Closer inspection reveals an intriguing application of the use of scale, in drawing the different specimens he has chosen to place in the same composition. Other styles that exhibit greater naiveté, in which lies much of the charm, can be seen in the plants drawn by William Young (pp.84-87) and the work of the artists who recorded the earliest years of the settlement of New South Wales (pp.42-51).

These collections also show that it is not only the work of the professional illustrator that stands the test of time. The amateur artist has contributed much to the natural art record. The sketch- books of Olivia Tonge (pp.90-97) reveal her to have been a keen observer with a sense of humour and a talent for painting. Tonge's style is distinctive and her sketch-books unique but the collection holds many other volumes by amateur artists whose work both delights and informs. By contrast Edward Lear (pp.82-83) was a professional illustrator who over time has become better known for his verse, which he started as a diversion, and whose artistic triumphs are not so widely appreciated.

The final aim in making this selection was simply to bring to the attention of a wider audience the existence of these wonderful, diverse, largely unknown treasures. The pictures were selected to try and represent the range of the whole collection. With space for only 70 items we have inevitably had to leave out many works which would further show this diversity and which in terms of quality, interest and importance could justly have been included. Similarly, the small biographical passages and quotes are meant but to whet the appetite. As with most encounters with the natural world it is hoped that these discoveries will inspire the reader to want to find out much more.

Christopher Mills
Head of Collections and Reader Services
The Natural History Museum

Note on Sir Joseph Banks

1743-1820
London

In the biographies that follow the name of Sir Joseph Banks occurs a number of times. He was not an artist but he was a formidable scientist and great patron and sponsor. A wealthy Lincolnshire landowner he was interested in natural history from an early age. When the Endeavour was being prepared for Cook's first voyage, Banks approached the Admiralty and requested to be allowed to accompany the expedition. His request was agreed to and when the Endeavour sailed Banks and his team of scientists and illustrators were among the company.

After the initial objective of the voyage – the observation of The Transit of Venus from Tahiti – had been achieved, Cook sailed further south in the Pacific and alighted upon the east coast of Australia. Banks and his colleagues collected thousands of specimens and made many hundreds of drawings. This was in many respects the first of the great scientific voyages and set a model for a number of subsequent expeditions.

After his return from this voyage Banks went on to become the youngest and longest serving President of The Royal Society. He was effectively the Director of the Botanic Gardens at Kew and instrumental in developing it into a great scientific institution. He amassed a library and specimen collection without parallel which eventually passed to the British Museum. When the natural history collections were transferred from Bloomsbury to South Kensington most of this material was also relocated. As well as purchasing items he also organised and sponsored many collecting trips and voyages and can be said to be directly or indirectly responsible for a significant proportion of the great scientific art of the late eighteenth and early nineteenth centuries.

Arthur Harry Church

1865-1937
Born Plymouth, Devon

On the death of his mother, Arthur Harry Church, aged twenty, inherited £100 which enabled him to go to University College, Aberystwyth. Four years later he won one of two scholarships to Queen's and Jesus Colleges Oxford, where, in 1894, he graduated with First Class Honours in botany. Church was a Research Fellow at Jesus College from 1908 to 1912 and was elected a Fellow of the Royal Society in 1921. He continued to work as a Demonstrator in the Department of Botany at Jesus College until 1930.

Church specialised in comparative plant morphology and was a master of microtechnique. His work in both theoretical and practical aspects of botany was highly original and is considered by many as revolutionary. His artwork is no less original. It accompanied his book *Types of floral mechanism* and is notable for the wealth of colour contrasted by black and white illustrations.

Church always insisted on the subject he was painting being perfect. He had no desire to draw plants half eaten by bugs. Each drawing was correctly scaled at a magnification sufficient to show the smallest detail required, which in flowers he considered to be the ovule. He regarded the use of Chinese white as the only way to capture natural brilliance. Ovules were modelled as blobs of Chinese white, then shaved with a razor when dry for a smooth surface.

His drawings are considered as some of the finest of their type ever produced in the twentieth century, and as an artist he has been compared with the Bauer brothers. Church himself studied Ferdinand Bauer's use of paint in the originals for Sibthorp's *Flora graeca*.

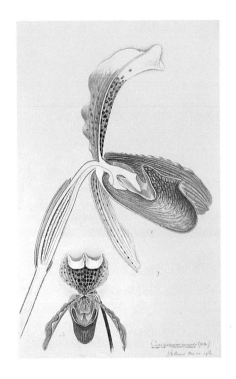

CHURCH, Arthur Harry

Cypripedium insigne
Slipper orchid

Magnification x3
Watercolour
310 x 200 mm
1906

Cleome spinosa
Spider flower

Magnification x3
Watercolour
315 x 195 mm
1909

Ophrys purpurea
Orchid

Magnification x6
Watercolour
190 x 320 mm
1906

Masdevallia chimaera
Orchid

Magnification x2
Watercolour
320 x 195 mm
1912

Papaver somniferum (×2) (var.)

A.H. Church del July 7 1904.

10

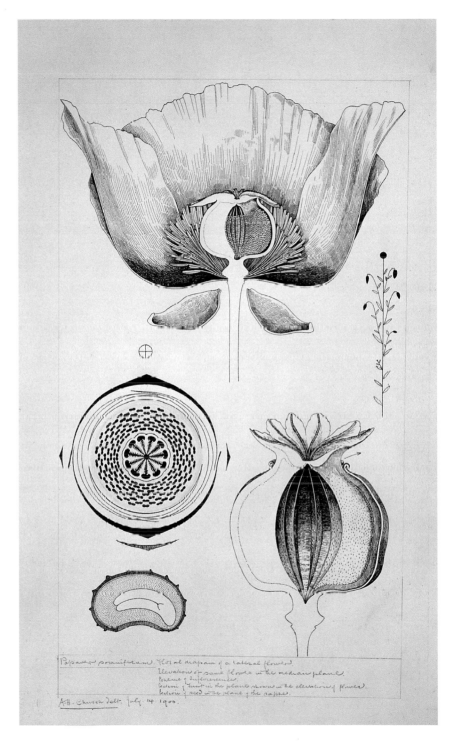

CHURCH, Arthur Harry

Papaver somniferum
Opium poppy

Magnification x2
Watercolour
190 x 320 mm
1904

Papaver somniferum
Opium poppy

Pen and ink
318 x 190 mm
1900

CHURCH, Arthur Harry

Althaea rosea
Hollyhock

Magnification x3
Watercolour
315 x 190 mm
1904

Galanthus elwesii
Snowdrop

Magnification x4
Watercolour
315 x 190 mm
1906

Althaea rosea (L.) Cav

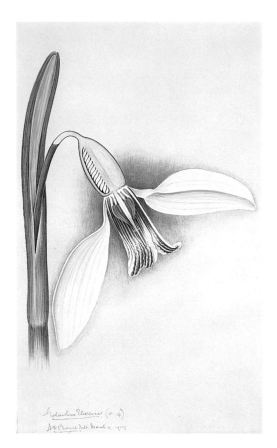

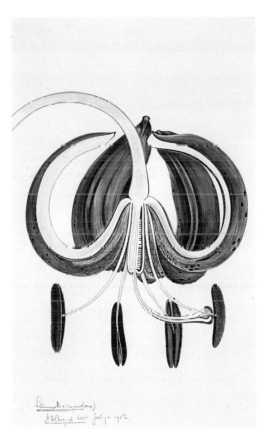

CHURCH, Arthur Harry

Lilium umbellatum
Lily

Magnification x2.5
Watercolour
320 x 205 mm
1903

Lilium martagon
Turk's cap lily

Magnification x4
Watercolour
315 x 205 mm
1906

CHURCH, Arthur Harry

Odontoglossum alexandrea
Orchid
Bombus terrestris
Bumble bee

Magnification x4
Watercolour
230 x 190 mm
1907

Cypripedium calceolus
Slipper orchid

Magnification x3
Watercolour
320 x 200 mm
1912

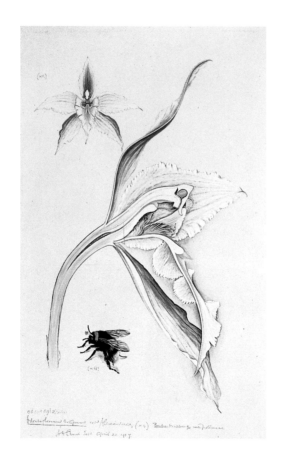

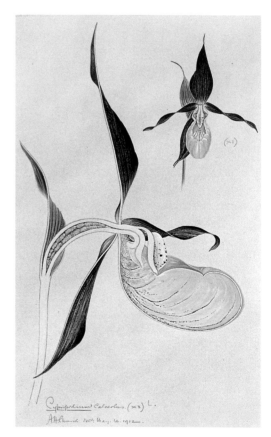

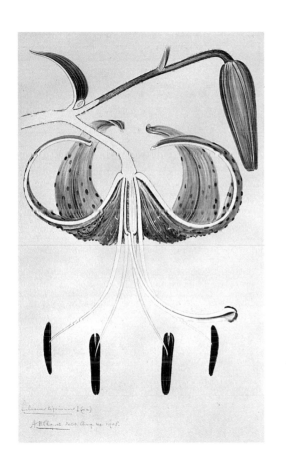

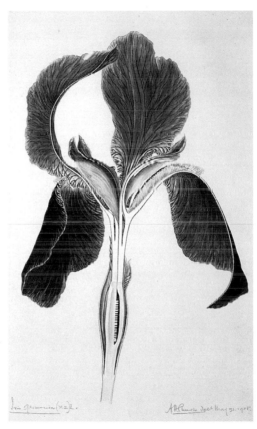

CHURCH, Arthur Harry

Lilium tigrinum
Tiger lily

Magnification x2
Watercolour
320 x 200 mm
1908

Iris germanica
London or purple flag

Magnification x2
Watercolour
320 x 204 mm
1908

Nymphaea alba t-ssp. alba.

Nymphaea alba (×2)

A.H. Church delt. July 1907-8.

"*Until one has drawn it is impossible to understand.*"

A.H. Church

16

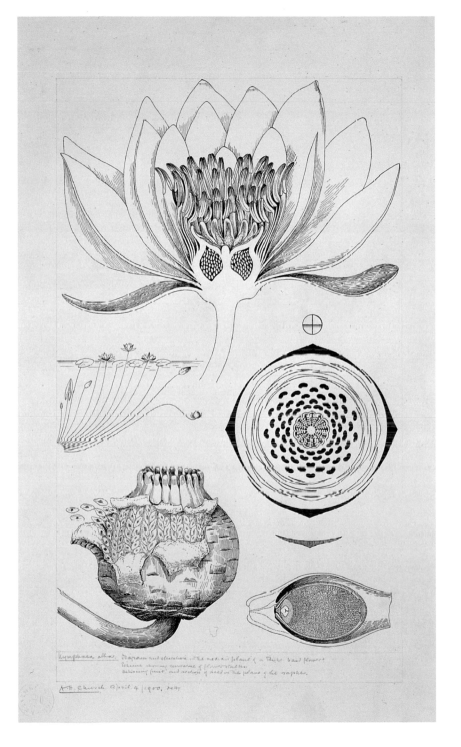

CHURCH, Arthur Harry

Nymphaea alba
Water lily

Magnification x2
Watercolour
195 x 315 mm
1907/8

Nymphaea alba
Water lily

Pen and ink
316 x 192 mm
1900

C.G. Finch-Davies.
19-4-18

18

Claude Gibney Finch-Davies

1875-1920
Born Delhi, India

FINCH-DAVIES, Claude
Gibney

Vanellus armatus
Blacksmith Plover, male

Pencil and watercolour
177 x 255 mm
1918

Claude Gibney Finch-Davies was the son of Major-General Sir William Davies, briefly Governor of Delhi and Lady E.B. Davies. The latter had a keen interest in natural history, particularly snakes, and it is likely that young Claude's own interest was nurtured by his mother. From an early age he developed a particular interest in birds, evidenced by the fact that soon after he was sent to school in England, aged six, he was sending his older sisters in India, paintings of birds as presents.

He did not do well academically and at eighteen was sent to enrol with the Cape Mounted Riflemen in the Cape Province of southern Africa. He spent the rest of his life in Africa. His duties sent him right across the sub-continent and gave him an excellent opportunity to follow his interest in avifauna. He spent much of his free time studying and painting and over a period of twenty years filled over 30 sketch books with carefully executed drawings and notes.

In 1915 shortly after becoming a lieutenant he met his future wife, Aileen Singleton Finch. The appropriateness of his wife's surname caused much amusement among his friends. On marriage in 1916 his in-laws insisted he adopt their surname and Davies became Finch-Davies.

We know relatively little about Finch-Davies, although through the pages of his sketchbooks we get some idea of his life in an army camp as he records events of this time alongside his observations on birds. Most of his drawings are now to be found in institutions in South Africa, but The Natural History Museum possesses one of his sketchbooks containing 21 beautiful drawings of birds in pencil and watercolour, made between 1918 and 1920, and their associated field notes.

Very little of his work was published, but 69 plates were used to illustrate Major Boyd Horsbrugh's *Game birds and water fowl of South Africa* published in 1912. Many of the drawings from the sketchbooks in South Africa appeared in *The birds of South Africa* 1982.

Dutch Paintings Collection

The paintings in this collection, all watercolours, are good examples of the floral illustration Holland is renowned for from the seventeenth and eighteenth centuries. The perfection of the flowers depicted may well be suspect because the artists may only rarely have seen unblemished flowers, such was the scourge of plant diseases at the time. Often, they would use imagination and artistic license to create that perfect bloom.

The tulip had only been introduced to western Europe's botanical literature in 1561 and its first serious description was not until 1601, by Clusius. The novelty of tulips was at its peak, leading to Tulipomania in the mid-seventeenth century, when prices were astronomical and the allure of a painting was causing a floral passion we cannot probably appreciate today. The desire to own tulips was so strong that many gardens were broken into and robbed of their prize bulbs.

These gifted still life painters were working in Haarlem, Leiden, Antwerp and Rotterdam, but we have little information about them.

VAN der VINNE, Jan Laurenszoom

Tulipa
Tulips

Watercolour with ink border
124 x 180 mm
ca 1730

VAN HUYSUM, Maria

Peaches and plums

Watercolour
206 x 327 mm
ca 17??

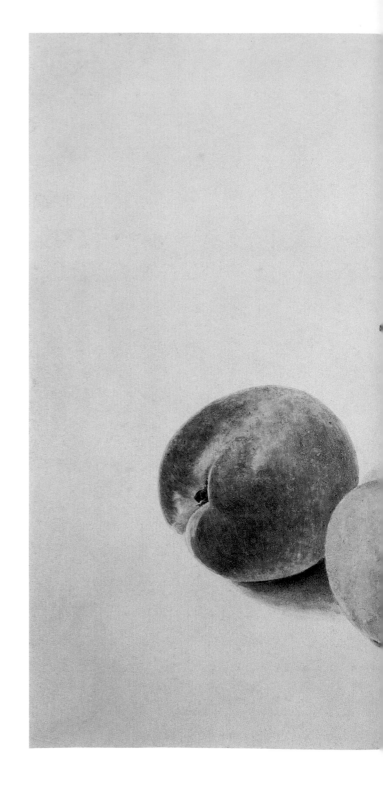

"Nature keeps whatever she has done best close sealed, until it is regarded with reverence."
John Ruskin

John Lindley

1799-1865
Born Catton, Norfolk

John Lindley began his career working as an assistant in the library of Sir Joseph Banks, but soon moved to the Chiswick Garden of the Horticultural Society of London to work as a clerk. Lindley eventually served as secretary to the Society from 1858 to 1863 and in recognition of his services, The Royal Horticultural Society library is named after him.

Lindley earned a Ph.D. degree from the University of Munich and later became Professor of Botany at University College London from 1829 to 1860. During his career he authored many taxonomic studies as well as textbooks on botany.

Lindley was first and foremost a botanist but his keen sense of observation led him at an early age to turn to drawing many of his specimens. His style, of which this illustration is typical, is similar to that of many botanists of the time who also turned their hand to drawing.

"Fresh blown flowers are and ever have been the symbol of joy."
William Bartram

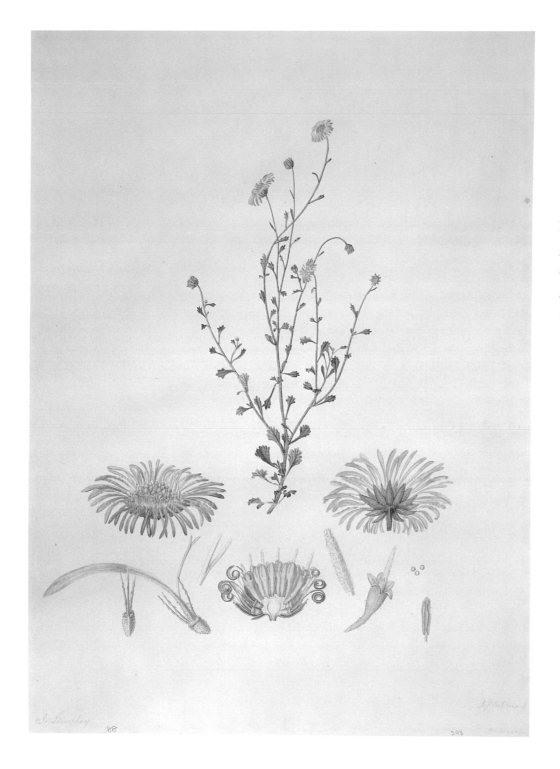

LINDLEY, John

Diplostemma

Watercolour
488 x 348 mm
ca 1840

William Bartram

1739-1823
Born Kinsessing, Philadelphia

William Bartram was the fifth son of John Bartram, a Quaker and the King's botanist in America. Both father and son are considered to be the first American natural scientists.

William continued the work his father had begun investigating the flora and fauna of America. In 1774 he travelled along the Appalachians, through North and South Carolina, Georgia, Florida and Alabama collecting specimens, writing and drawing whilst living with the Native Americans of these regions. In South Georgia he collected the only known specimen of ever found growing in the wild.

Many of the plants and animals drawn by Bartram were previously unknown to science and some of his drawings are considered 'type-specimens' in lieu of an actual specimen preserved elsewhere. His drawings and specimens were sent to England to his patron, the English Quaker physician and botanist Dr. John Fothergill. After Fothergill's death in 1780 Sir Joseph Banks acquired the Fothergill herbarium along with Bartram's plants and drawings, including the two drawings exhibited here which were made between 1768 and 1776.

Both Banks and the librarian and botanical curator of his collections, Daniel Solander, were preoccupied with recording the more exotic flora of the East so it was not until years later, after the death of Banks and the transfer of the collection to the British Museum, that Bartram's plants were studied. The recognition Bartram sought when he expressed the desire for the "bare mention of my being the discoverer" of new plants, was never achieved during his lifetime.

The attraction of Bartram's drawings for many is the interesting use of scale and humour.

BARTRAM, William

Nelumbo lutea
American lotus seed vessel
Triodopsis albolabris
Snail

Ink and watercolour
240 x 300 mm
ca 1775

Tab. 1.

28

BARTRAM, William

Nelumbo lutea
American lotus or water
chinquapin
Dionaea muscipula
Venus flytrap
Ardea herodius
Great blue heron

Ink
397 x 300 mm
ca 1772

"…*admirable are the properties of the extraordinary Dionaea muscipula… those sportive vegetables… they are organical, living and self moving bodies, for we see here, in this plant, motion and volition.*"

William Bartram, *Travels*, 1791

Claire Dalby

1944-
Born St. Andrews, Fife

Claire Dalby was elected to the Royal Watercolour Society in 1973 and the Royal Society of Painter-Printmakers in 1978. In 1974 she was awarded the Jill Smythies prize by the Linnean Society of London for published botanical illustrations. The same year she became vice-president for the Royal Watercolour Society.

Dalby has published a number of illustrated works that have been used for educational purposes. She has exhibited throughout the country and has also taught botanical illustration at the Royal Botanic Gardens at Kew and Edinburgh, and Cambridge University Botanic Garden. Dalby is not only a botanical illustrator but also a wood engraver.

Her work is to be found in the collections of many important institutions such as the Victoria and Albert Museum, National Museum and Gallery of Wales, Ashmolean Museum, Oxford and the Hunt Institute for Botanical Documentation, Pittsburgh.

DALBY, Claire

Lecanora poliophaea
Lichen

Watercolour and pencil
185 x 198 mm
1980

Caloplaca verruculifera
Lichen

Watercolour and pencil
180 x 172 mm
1981

Caloplaca
verruculifera
– Claire Dalby 1981

31

John Fullwood

1854-1931
Place of birth unknown

John Fullwood was a well-known landscape painter of his day who was also noted for his copperplate etching. He studied in London, Paris and Berlin and was a member of many societies, including the Royal Society of Arts, Birmingham. As a hobby, Fullwood studied geology and was fond of making drawings of the pebbles he collected from beaches around Britain.

Fullwood was a regular exhibitor at the Royal Academy and was one of the artists invited to contribute to a folio of works for the Queen's Doll's House, which was exhibited in aid of charities at the British Empire Exhibition, Wembley. He painted a landscape whose overall size, including the frame, measured only two inches by three inches. Many of his pictures of pebbles resemble miniature landscapes in themselves.

"…epics in each pebble underneath our feet."

Charles Kingsley, *The invitation to Tom Hughes*

FULLWOOD, John

Pebbles found on British beaches

Watercolour
140 x 89 mm
Dates unknown

"…won his honours so entirely by his industry

J. Pope Rogers 1880

Henry Bone

1755-1834
Born Truro, Cornwall

BONE, Henry

Various copper ores

Watercolour
201 x 254 mm
ca 1795

Original drawing for a
plate in Rashleigh, Philip
1797, *Specimens of British
Minerals...* London

Henry Bone's father was a cabinet maker and carver. When Henry was twelve, his family moved to Plymouth and he was apprenticed to William Cooksworthy, the founder of the Plymouth porcelain works. Cooksworthy and his young apprentice moved to Bristol in 1771 to work for another manufacturer.

Henry took up art at night school, and specialised in china enamelling. His work from this period is held in high regard. Following the closure of the Bristol China Works in 1778 he moved to London, where he found employment enamelling watches and fans, later branching out into enamel and watercolour portraits as these came into fashion. He also made the drawings for Philip Rashleigh's *Specimens of British Minerals selected from the Cabinet of Philip Rashleigh of Menabilly, in the County of Cornwall, with general descriptions of each article*. Rashleigh was one of the most important mineral collectors of the eighteenth century. He amassed a wealth of specimens from all over Great Britain, in particular from Cornwall, and it is now one of the few great collections of this time to remain largely intact.

In 1800 Bone was appointed enamel painter to the Prince of Wales, and in 1811 elected to the Royal Academy. He continued working to great acclaim until his eyesight failed in 1831, thereafter reluctantly retiring on a Royal Academy pension. Before his death he offered his collection to the nation for £4,000, when its value was £10,000, but the offer was declined and the collection was sadly dispersed on his death.

and skill in the pursuit of an attractive art..."

Brian Hargreaves

19??-
Born Sutton-in-Craven, Yorkshire

Brian Hargreaves studied at Camberwell School of Art and Crafts. He then worked for a number of years on church restoration, including gilding the ball and cross on St Paul's Cathedral. Whilst working on display material for The Natural History Museum, he was asked to do specimen illustrations of butterflies and was commissioned to produce the internationally acclaimed illustrations for *Collin's A field guide to the butterflies of Britain and Europe.*

Hargreaves drew nearly 800 butterflies for this work, developing an unusual technique to do so. In an attempt to reproduce the effect of scales on the butterfly wing he combined watercolour pencils and coloured inks. Each butterfly drawing required between half a day and two days to complete and the project took a total of three and a half years.

Since then he has illustrated 17 other books on butterflies, moths, caterpillars and pests and diseases of garden plants, two of which gained him gold medals from the Royal Horticultural Society. He was recently commissioned by the Royal Entomological Society to illustrate the Gardens of Buckingham Palace for the Queen, showing many of the butterflies found there.

HARGREAVES, Brian

Wildlife Garden,
The Natural History
Museum, London
Celastrina argiolus
Holly blue
Vanessa atalanta
Red admiral
Vanessa cardui
Painted lady
Libellula depressa
Broad-bodied chaser

Watercolour
356 x 255 mm
1997

HARGREAVES, Brian

Family *Lycaenidae*
Hairstreak butterflies

Watercolour pencil and
coloured ink
353 x 260 mm
ca 1974
Original drawing for a
plate in *A field guide to
the butterflies of the West
Indies.*

HARGREAVES, Brian

Family *Pieridae*
Sulphur butterflies

Watercolour pencil and
coloured ink
353 x 260 mm
ca 1974
Original drawing for a
plate in *A field guide to
the butterflies of the West
Indies.*

HARGREAVES, Brian

Family *Pieridae*
Clouded yellow butterflies

Watercolour pencil and
coloured ink
339 x 232 mm
ca 1968
Original drawings for a
plate in *A field guide to
the butterflies of Britain
and Europe.*

40

HARGREAVES, Brian

Family *Nymphalidae*

Watercolour pencil and
coloured ink
339 x 232 mm
ca 1968
Original drawings for a
plate in *A field guide to
the butterflies of Britain
and Europe.*

George Raper

ca 1767-1797
Born London, England

Thomas Watling

1762-ca1806
Born Dumfries, Scotland

The Port Jackson Painter

An unknown artist

The Natural History Museum Library contains a wealth of important original artwork relating to the early exploration and colonisation of Australia, and the unfolding of the fascinating and exotic flora and fauna of that continent.

The Raper Collection of watercolour paintings of the topography and natural history of New South Wales and Norfolk Island is the work of George Raper, midshipman on HMS Sirius which sailed with the First Fleet in May 1787, taking convicts to the new colony. Considering that Raper was not a trained artist and still only twenty-four when he returned to England, the paintings are extremely accomplished.

The Watling and Port Jackson Painter Collections are a large body of paintings thought to represent the work of several artists. The identity and number of artists involved is uncertain and remains a controversy.

Thomas Watling was a trained artist who was convicted of forgery and sentenced to deportation. He arrived in Port Jackson (now Sydney) in 1792. His artistic abilities were recognised by the colony's first governor, Arthur Phillip, and he was put to work to draw the landscapes, flora and fauna of the Port Jackson area. Many paintings in the Collection are signed by Watling, but a considerable number are the work of at least one other artist, often referred to as the Port Jackson Painter.

Many theories have been put forward as to the identity of the Port Jackson Painter, one being that it was Henry Brewer (1739-1796), also a midshipman on HMS Sirius. It may indeed be that the Port Jackson style represents several artists including pupils or copyists. Whatever the truth, one point is certain, that the paintings represent a unique resource for historians, scientists and art scholars.

COCKATOO of PORT-JACKSON. *Natural Size* H.Raper. 1789 –

RAPER, George
Cockatoo of Port Jackson

Calyptorhynchus lathami
Glossy cockatoo, female

Natural size
Watercolour
495 x 315 mm
1789

Ban nel lang meeting the Governor by appointment after he was wounded by Wil le ma rin in September 1790

44

Port Jackson Painter

Ban nel lang meeting the
Governor by appointment
after he was wounded by
Wil le ma ring in
September 1790

Watercolour
263 x 403 mm
ca 1790

"Holy Mother Earth, the trees and all nature, are witnesses of your thoughts and deeds."
A Winnebago wise saying.

1. Musical Instruments made of hard wood Crested Saw on very
2. A Club made of ... d.°...

Port Jackson Painter

Musical Instruments
and a club

Ink and watercolour
344 x 200 mm
ca 1790

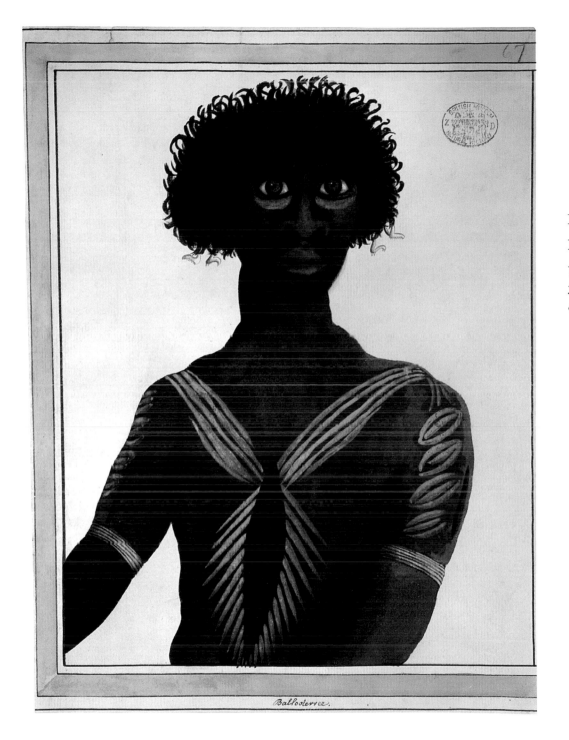

Balloderree.

Port Jackson Painter

Balloderree

Ink and watercolour
286 x 212 mm
ca 1790

WATLING, Thomas

Pogona barbata
Bearded dragon

Watercolour
177 x 296 mm
ca 1790

"…In all things of nature there is something of the marvellous…"
Aristotle, *On the parts of animals*

"The solitudes of nature were my school,
And in the moaning voice of streams and winds,
Without the aid of dull scholastic rule,
I felt the tone which in the lone heart finds its echo."

William MacGillivray

GUM-PLANT, & KANGOOROO of NEW-HOLLAND ~ Reduced size ~ *G. Raper* 1789 ~

RAPER, George

Gum plant and kangaroo
of New Holland

Macropus giganteus
Eastern grey kangaroo
Xanthorrhoea
Grasstree

Ink and watercolour
466 x 326 mm
1789

Amadeo John Engel Terzi

1872-1956
Born Palermo, Sicilly

Amadeo Terzi was born into a family of illustrators who nurtured his natural talent for art. He had no formal training, but is now widely regarded as a very fine entomological artist.

He embarked on his career in scientific illustration chiefly as a result of his acquaintance with the Italian entomologist Louis Sambon, who worked at the London School of Tropical Medicine and had a pivotal role in the experiment carried out in Italy in 1900 to test the theory of malarial transmission by mosquitoes. Terzi was engaged by Sambon to illustrate the resulting paper and he also had the dubious honour of being one of the 'guinea pigs' in the experiment. He and two others spent four months living in an area notorious for malaria, their only protection being a specially built tent with fine mesh screens designed to keep the mosquitoes out at night. Luckily the tents worked, Terzi and his colleagues remained healthy and the role of mosquitoes in the transmission of malaria was finally established.

Terzi's work on this paper secured him a post as an illustrator at the London School of Tropical Medicine, where he stayed for a year before being invited to join the staff of The Natural History Museum, in 1902. He remained at the Museum for the rest of his working life, during which time he completed over 37,000 drawings, illustrating over 50 books and more than 500 scientific papers.

TERZI, Amadeo

Tabanus autumnalis
Horsefly

Watercolour
316 x 445 mm
ca 1905

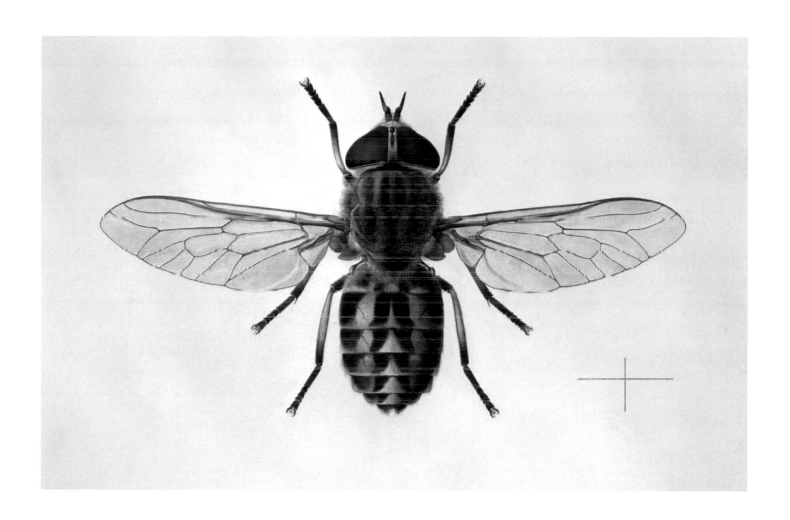

"the student who is interested in entomological illustration… will find no better teacher."

G. F. Ferris 1928, *The principles of systematic entomology*, Stanford

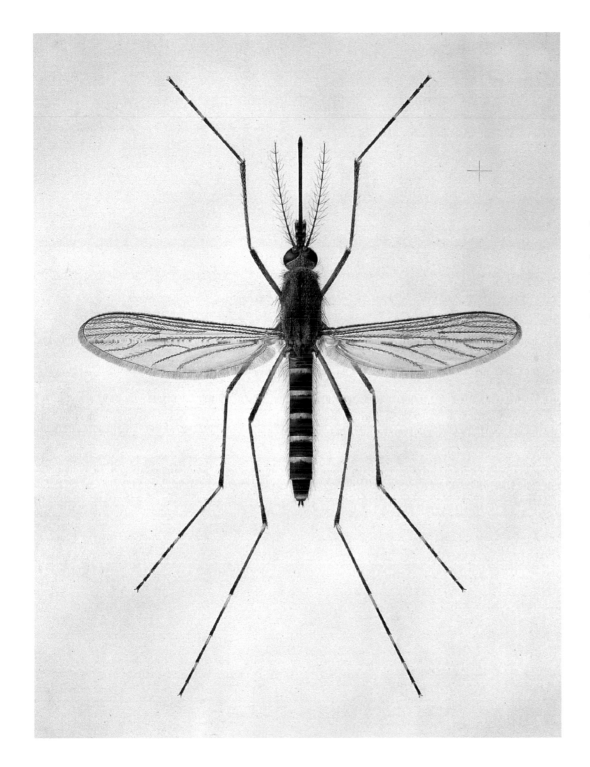

TERZI, Amadeo

Aedes cantans
Mosquito

Watercolour
445 x 316 mm
ca 1937

EHRET, Georg Dionysius

Punica granatum
Pomegranate

Watercolour
511 x 372 mm
1742

PUNICA *quæ malum granatum fert. Cafalp.*

Georg Dionysius Ehret

1708-1770
Born Heidelberg, Germany

Georg Ehret was born into a family of gardeners, and himself became a gardener's apprentice. His apprenticeship continued for several years before he was employed to work in the gardens of the Margrave Karl III Wilhelm at Karlsruhe. During this time Ehret taught himself the technique of watercolour. His paintings were well received by the Margrave and Ehret was given preferential treatment. This aroused envy amongst the other gardeners and eventually Ehret was forced to tender his resignation.

He decided to give up gardening at the age of twenty-three to become a painter and botanist. After much hardship, he managed to sell some drawings to a wealthy Nuremberg Physician, Christopher Jacob Trew, who recognised Ehret's talent and became his patron and lifelong friend.

Ehret made his way to Paris, covering much of the ground on foot, and finding work by drawing plants from large gardens as he went. He continued as an itinerant botanical artist and in 1736 travelled to Holland, to meet the Swedish botanist Linnaeus. Later that same year Ehret returned to England where he married and settled for the rest of his life.

A number of Ehret's works are on vellum which he much preferred to paper. In his drawings he enlarged many of the smaller plants and his use of colour was not always a slavish imitation of what he saw. His work is considered to be a compromise between that of an artist and a scientist and is viewed approvingly by both. By the mid 1730s Ehret had virtually given up painting European species and was employed by various collectors to draw the multitude of newly introduced species arriving in Europe from all over the world.

Ehret had his own distinct style, he was a great draughtsman and his drawings have a quality of earthiness that distinguishes him from the poetic charm of the more famous botanical artist of his day, Redouté. Ehret's notebooks are some of the earliest in existence from any of the great botanical artists and as such are an important record of the way in which he and others of his time worked.

EHRET, Georg Dionysius

Picea glauca
White Spruce
Picea mariana
Black Spruce

Pencil and watercolour
298 x 213 mm
ca 1750s

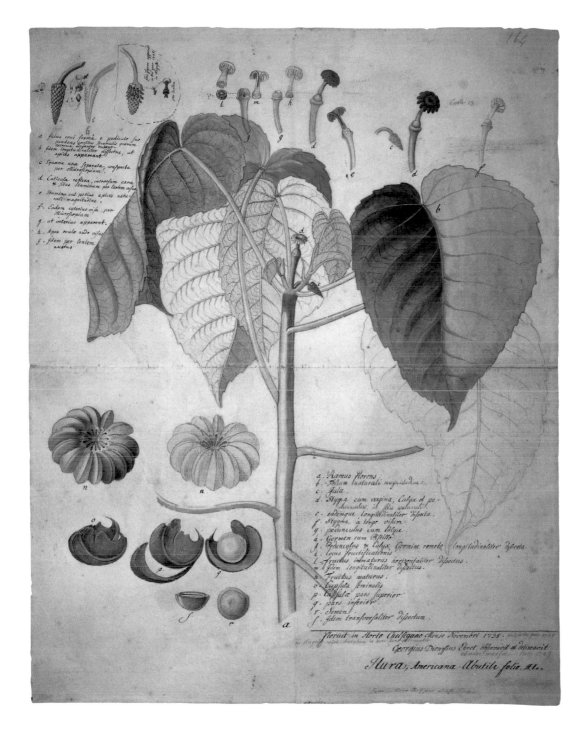

EHRET, Georg Dionysius

Hura crepitans

Pencil and watercolour
511 x 372 mm
ca 1740s

59

*"There is no better way of loving
nature than through art."*

Oscar Wilde

EHRET, Georg Dionysius

Zantedeschia aethiopica
Arum lily

Watercolour
608 x 447 mm
ca 1740s

Ferdinand Lucas Bauer

1760-1826
Born Feldsberg, Austria

Ferdinand Lucas Bauer was born into a family of painters. He was apprenticed to a distinguished physician, Norbert Boccius, Prior of the town's monastery, to make drawings of the plants growing in the monastery's botanical garden.

Ferdinand was working in Vienna when John Sibthorp, the Sherardian Professor of Botany at the University of Oxford, arrived in the city on his way to study the plants of Greece and Asia Minor in 1780. Bauer accompanied Sibthorp to Greece as botanical artist and returned with him to England. Although neither Sibthorp nor Ferdinand lived to see the *Flora graeca* (1806-40) completed, this magisterial work in 10 volumes containing 966 magnificent hand-coloured engraved plates after drawings by Ferdinand is one of the most beautiful of all botanical books.

In England, Bauer's paintings greatly impressed Sir Joseph Banks, who was seeking a competent natural history artist to join an expedition to survey the coasts of Australia. Bauer sailed from England in 1801 on the *Investigator* under the command of Matthew Flinders, with Robert Brown as the expedition's naturalist. Ferdinand was the perfect choice – experienced, competent, hardworking and productive. Whatever was collected from the surrounding land or dredged up from the sea and brought before him was all drawn with the same precision. The results of the expedition included 3000 plant specimens and 1500 drawings of plants and 230 drawings of animals.

In 1814, Bauer returned to Austria taking all the pencil drawings from the Investigator voyage with him. He left his finished watercolours in England. In addition to 203 botanical drawings he had completed 46 zoological watercolours and six pencil drawings of fish. However, this small sample illustrates some of the quintessential Australian fauna.

BAUER, Ferdinand

Platycercus adscitus
palliceps
Pale headed rosella

Watercolour
335 x 501 mm
ca 1811

BAUER, Ferdinand

Phascolarctos cinereus
Koala

Watercolour
511 x 340 mm
ca 1811

BAUER, Ferdinand

Vombatus ursinus
Wombat

Watercolour
512 x 336 mm
ca 1811

Henry Walter Bates

1825-1892
Born Leicester, England

Bates left school aged 13 but continued his education by attending evening classes at the local Mechanics' Institute where he studied Greek, Latin, French, Drawing and Composition. In 1844 he met Alfred Russell Wallace who shared his interest in natural history. They were both impressed by W.H. Edwards' work *A voyage up the Amazon*, published in 1847, and in 1848 they decided to undertake their own expedition to this region to collect insects and other natural history specimens.

Wallace returned to England in 1852 but Bates remained collecting on the Amazons for a total of 11 years. During this time he lived a very frugal life, selling specimens to dealers in Europe in order to survive, and filling the pages of his notebooks with careful observations and detailed drawings. He collected over 14,000 insect species of which 8,000 were new to science.

Bates returned to England and in 1862 presented his famous paper to the Linnean Society – *Contributions to an insect fauna of the Amazon Valley*. In this work he introduced the idea of insect mimicry. He noted that some harmless butterflies mimic species which are distasteful and so avoid attack from insectivorous birds. This form of mimicry is now known as Batesian Mimicry. Darwin was deeply impressed with this work which helped to further develop the theory of natural selection, and he encouraged Bates to write a detailed account of his travels. In 1863, *The naturalist on the River Amazons* was published and met with great scientific and popular acclaim.

BATES, Henry Walter

The Amazon Expedition

Manuscript ink notes, watercolour and pencil drawings
225 x 163 mm
ca 1851-1859

"Darwinian before Darwin."

Grant Allen

Franz Bauer

1758-1840
Born Feldsberg, Austria

Franz Bauer was one of five brothers, three of whom followed their father, Lucas Bauer, court painter to the Prince of Liechtenstein, into an artistic career.

Franz visited London in 1788 intending to travel on to Paris but in 1790 was offered a position at the Botanic Gardens at Kew, as Botanical Illustrator By Appointment, from Sir Joseph Banks. Bauer became the first paid botanical artist at Kew and remained there until his death in 1840. His salary was paid from Banks' own purse.

Whilst working at Kew, Bauer produced many thousands of illustrations, of which a sizeable collection is held in the Botany Library of The Natural History Museum.

Franz Bauer became a highly skilled botanist and extended his artwork to microscopic drawings. His work includes remarkable drawings of pollen grains, detailed drawings of plant diseases and the structure of orchids together with some of the most delicate and subtle paintings of flowers. Wilfried Blunt, author of *The art of botanical illustration*, and Georg Pritzel, the great German botanical bibliographer, both consider Franz Bauer to be the greatest botanical artist of all time.

Franz Bauer died at Kew and is buried in the churchyard there next to Gainsborough.

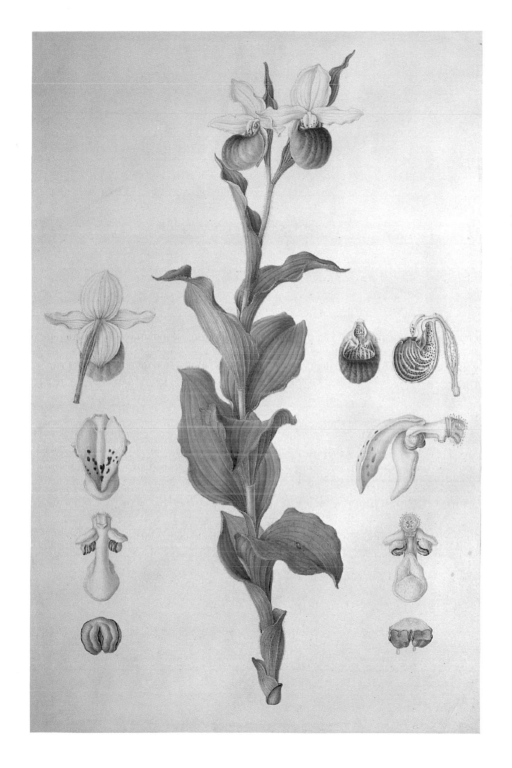

BAUER, Franz

Cypripedium spectabile
Lady's slipper orchid

Watercolour
487 x 317 mm
ca 1810-1840

"A thing of beauty is a joy for ever:
Its loveliness increases; it will
never pass into nothingness..."

John Keates – Endymion

BAUER, Franz

Paeonia
Peony

Watercolour
515 x 362 mm
ca 1810-1840

"In the delineation of plants he united the accuracy of the profound naturalist with the skill of the accomplished artist to a degree which has been only equalled by his brother Ferdinand."

Inscription on Franz Bauer's memorial at Kew.

BAUER, Franz

Apocynaceae plumeria
Frangipani

Watercolour
527 x 364 mm
ca 1810-1840

Alfred Waterhouse

1830-1905
Born Liverpool, England

Waterhouse was one of the most successful British architects of the second half of the nineteenth century. Although Waterhouse had really wanted to be an artist, his parents thought that architecture was a more suitable profession. Therefore after leaving school he was articled to an architectural practice in Manchester. In 1853 he started his own practice and established a large clientele in the north of England. Waterhouse moved to London in 1865, where his reputation continued to grow.

The commission to design a natural history museum in South Kensington was originally awarded to a Captain Fowkes who died before he could finalise his plans. Waterhouse was commissioned to complete the project but his finished building looks little like Fowkes' early design. The Natural History Museum is the greatest of his London buildings. With its Gothic towers, cathedral portal and dramatic halls, it is a major building of rare genius. The museum was completed in 1880 and opened to the public in 1881.

The inspired choice of terracotta for the facing of the building gave Waterhouse the opportunity to design a wealth of rich decoration inside and out. Waterhouse drew all the designs for the plants, animals and fossils that adorn the building. The modelled figures directly reflected the Museum's contents, with extinct species on the eastern wing and living species on the western wing. There are a total of 134 pencil drawings in the collection.

WATERHOUSE, Alfred

Caps of Piers in South galleries (West). Ground and first floor

Tyto alba
Barn owl
Bubo bubo
Great or Eagle owl

Pencil
270 x 370 mm
1878

T

The Barn Owl (*Strix flammea*)

The Great Owl *Bubo maximus*

Sent away July 17/78. C J Ill

Caps of piers in South Galleries (West) Ground & 1ˢᵗ floor

WATERHOUSE, Alfred

Panels in windows of first
floor, South Front (East)
Amblyrhynchus cristatus
Galapagos marine iguana

Pencil
265 x 375 mm
1875

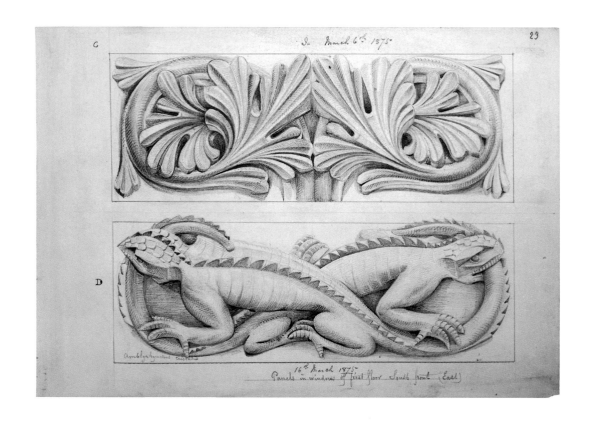

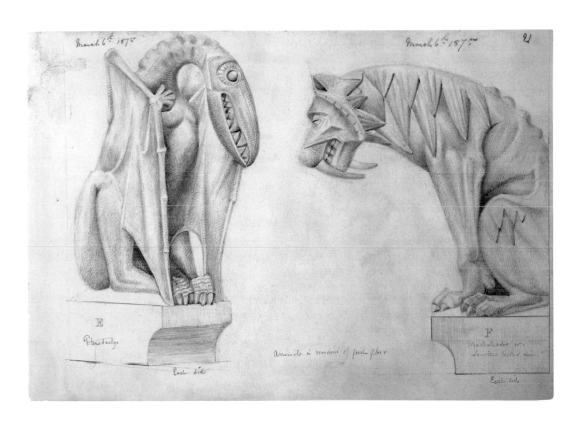

WATERHOUSE, Alfred

Animals in window of
first floor (East)
*Pterodactylus or
Dimorphodon*
Pterodactyl
Machairodus
Sabre toothed cat

Pencil
265 x 375 mm
1875

WATERHOUSE, Alfred

Annulet of shaft in
Entrance Hall

Pencil
265 x 366 mm
1875

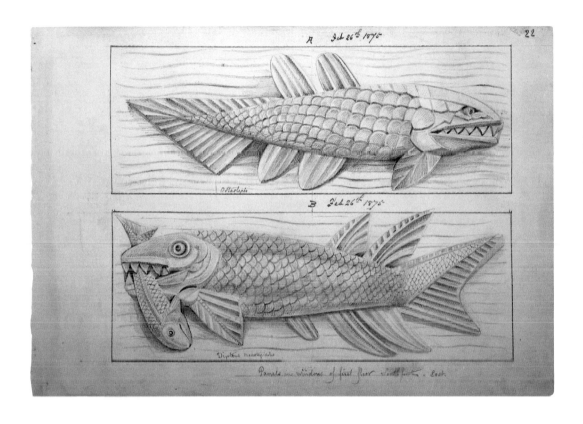

WATERHOUSE, Alfred

Panels in windows of first
floor. South front (East)
Osteolepis
Thursius macrolepidorus

Pencil
265 x 375 mm
1875

The Great Bustard (Otis tarda)

Panels

Sent Oct 30/78 Cp. J.

C

the Grey hound

principal Staircase) Index Museum (ground floor)

WATERHOUSE, Alfred

Panels in principal
staircase, Index Museum
ground floor

Otis tarda
Great bustard
Canis familiaris
Greyhound

Pencil
270 x 370 mm
1878

MACROCERCUS ARARAUNA.

Blue & Yellow Maccaw

⅓ Nat. Size.

E. Lear del et lith.

LEAR, Edward

Ara ararauna
Blue and yellow macaw

Hand coloured lithograph
555 x 365 mm
ca 1831

Edward Lear

1812-1888
Born Highgate, London

Today, Edward Lear is renowned for his comic verse and humorous sketches but he started his career as a painter of birds.

Lear was born in Highgate, in north London, the twentieth of twenty-one children and the son of a prosperous stockbroker. He was taught drawing by his elder sisters who were artistically accomplished. This was fortunate for the young Edward who unexpectedly found himself having to earn his living at the age of fifteen when the family's fortune crashed.

A commission from the Zoological Society to make drawings of animals living in its menagerie in Regent's Park for a guidebook was the inspiration for his first and only natural history book, *Illustrations of the family of Psittacidae, or Parrots* (1830-32). These vividly-coloured birds and their amusing antics appealed to Lear's sensitivity so much that he embarked on a book about them, intending to depict every variety. He persuaded the birds' keepers to hold them still while he painted and sketched. Back at his home in nearby Albany Street he perfected his sketches and then proceeded to copy the outlines onto massive lithographic stones.

In 1830 lithography was just emerging as a new method for book illustration. It had many advantages over the older technique of engraving not least the ability to convey the natural lustre and softness of bird plumage. When published these hand-coloured lithographic bird prints surpassed anything that had ever been seen before and Lear's work was accorded the highest praise. Unfortunately, Lear was unable to sell enough copies to cover the cost of production and he abandoned the project after the forty-second print was issued.

For a few years Lear supported himself by drawing birds and other animals for others, including the ornithologist John Gould until the time he left England to take up residence in Italy. It was whilst working for the Earl of Derby, drawing the animals in his menagerie at Knowsley Hall, that Lear started to produce his nonsense verse to entertain the Earl's children.

William Young

1742-1785
Born Hesse, Germany

William Young was a nurseryman from Philadelphia, where his immigrant German family had settled in 1751. Little of any certainty is known about him but it is recorded that his family originated in England and moved to Germany in 1556 due to religious persecution.

Young spent a lot of his time in the field recording and collecting plants. He discovered and sent back to England the first specimens of the Venus fly-trap from North Carolina and became botanist to King George III and Queen Charlotte in 1764. He also supplied plants and seeds to nurserymen and seedsmen for the London market.

During 1767 Young made an extensive plant collecting trip to North and South Carolina and from among the hundreds of specimens gathered he painted 302 watercolours. Although naive in style, and at times crude, some now represent type specimens long ago lost or destroyed. In 1768 he took live plants in casks to England from America and while there he presented the watercolours to the British Museum.

In 1782 he published his only catalogue of American plants, the *Catalogue d'arbres arbustes et plantes herbacees d'Amerique*, which was printed in Paris. It is the earliest known book on American botany by an American botanist, although Young did not use Linnean classification.

He died in 1785, drowning in Gunpowder Creek whilst on field work. His body lay undiscovered for seven weeks.

YOUNG, William

Plant numbers 134-136

Watercolour
383 x 240 mm
ca 1767

YOUNG, William

Plant numbers 140-142

Watercolour
384 x 241 mm
ca 1767

YOUNG, William

Plant numbers 108-110

Watercolour
383 x 240 mm
ca 1767

Bryan Kneale

1930 -
Born Douglas, Isle of Man

Bryan Kneale was born and grew up in the Isle of Man. He moved to London in 1948 to study at the Royal Academy Schools. The following year he won the Rome Prize in Painting and went to Italy where he stayed until 1951. He began exhibiting in 1954.

Originally studying drawing, he took up sculpture in 1958 and has worked extensively in both media ever since. He has had a distinguished academic career, holding the post of Professor of Sculpture at the Royal College of Art and Professor of Drawing at the Royal Academy. He was elected to the Royal Academy in 1970.

He has had over forty exhibitions, half of these being one-man shows and, whilst the majority of his material is in Britain, he has work in art collections all over the world, including the Museum of Modern Art in New York and the National Gallery of New Zealand.

It was while he was at the Royal College of Art, which is close to The Natural History Museum, that Kneale was encouraged by the Keeper of Zoology to work in the Museum. The work illustrated is one of the 'bone drawings' that resulted from the association.

Now retired and living in London, Bryan Kneale continues to be involved with various artistic projects and is currently working on the bronze doors at Portsmouth Cathedral.

KNEALE, Bryan

Geochelone
Giant Tortoise

Chalk
1100 mm x 800 mm
1990

"...more like architecture than organism, like huge structures composed of intelligence and feeling."

Philip Pullman, *The Subtle Knife* 1997

88

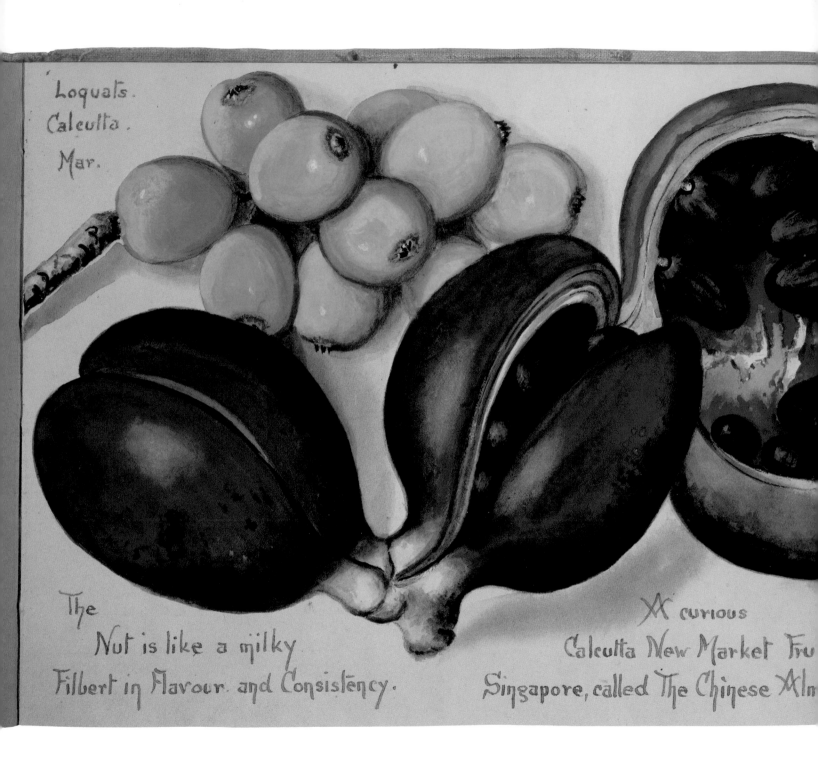

Loquats.
Calcutta.
Mar.

The
Nut is like a milky
Filbert in flavour and Consistency.

XX curious
Calcutta New Market Fru
Singapore, called The Chinese Aln

Olivia Fanny Tonge

1858-1949
Born Llandilotalybont, Glamorgan

TONGE, Olivia Fanny

Sterculia
Chinese Almond
Eriobotrya japonica
Loquat

Watercolour
180 x 260 mm
ca 1910

Olivia Fanny Fitzmaurice was born in Llandilotalybont, Glamorgan, of a naval family. Her grandfather served on the *Victory* at Trafalgar and her father had explored the coast of Australia where three rivers are named after him. He was also a keen naturalist and painter. As she was unable to draw landscapes, Olivia's father lost interest in her as a painter, but it was not appreciated that this inability was due to myopia rather than lack of talent. Olivia was in fact an accomplished watercolour painter from an early age, specialising in natural history subjects which she could see!

She married in 1878 and had two daughters. Following their birth there was a period of several years in which she did little painting. After her husband's early death she took up a wide range of artistic pursuits, including woodcarving, metalwork, dress designing, embroidery and singing.

She visited and lived in India during the years 1908-1910 and 1912-1913, where she returned to her painting. The result was a series of sixteen sketchbooks which were presented to the Museum in 1952. Her sketchbooks record objects that she saw in the market places of Sind, Karachi, Calcutta and Darjeeling along with examples of the local flora and fauna. This eclectic mix is interspersed with occasional delightful observations such as that next to the drawing of a wall gecko – "with tail slightly under repair". On her return from India she again ceased painting and transferred her skill to gardening. Olivia Tonge died in Lincoln at the age of ninety.

The
Oceanic Swimming Crab,
Neptúnus pelágicus.
A Crab that swims with the
grace of a Swallow's flight.

Albatross

sustai

feeds

Prey,

with the S

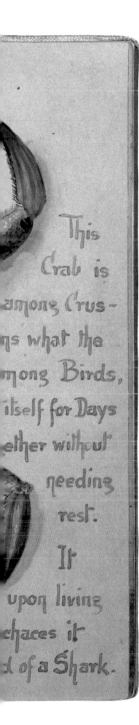

TONGE, Olivia Fanny

Portunus cf pelagicus
Oceanic swimming crab

Watercolour
180 x 260 mm
ca 1910

*"And it came to pass, that a certain Grandmother,
When that she had come to nigh on two score
years and ten, and had gotten long in the tooth,
spake unto herself thus, – …*

The Tesselated Parrot Fish,
Scarus harid.
called by the Natives
Laboo Girawah.
Karachi
Harbour.

TONGE, Olivia Fanny

The Tesselated Parrot Fish

Scarus ghobban
Bluebarred parrotfish

Watercolour
180 x 260 mm
ca 1910

"… *Lo, will I now paint. And she took much gold, yea, much fine gold, and gat her a book, and in the book, so that all men might see, painted she all the things that crawled upon the face of the earth, and all things seemly, lo, that flew in the air, and all the things that swam in the waters that are under the earth,…*

The Gold Torc, set with Pearls, Rubies, and Emeralds, and weighing Two Pounds, belonging to the Dowager Begum of Las Bela, Baluchistan.

A Purdah Lady of the Begum's Rank must not expose her Face to any Man, except nearest relatives.

The Camel Wallah leads the Purdah Lady's Camel every step of the way to Las Bela, 100 Miles or so.

Nose Ring belonging to the Las Bela Family.

Th

Beg

from K

a fearful Jo

attended the Thir

the Jam of Las Bela. The Jam ta

Girl Wife every Three Years or so. The

The Mahommedan Religion allows hir

96

what the
ravelled in
hi To Las Bela,
ey, when she
arriage of
a new little
s his Third.
t another.

TONGE, Olivia Fanny

Jewellery made of gold
and precious stones

Watercolour
180 x 260 mm
ca 1912

*"… and things of divers handicraft painted she,
yea, even nose rings and rings for the toes
painted she, until the people were wearied of her
works, and verily no man mote stop her."*

Curious Fragment Tonge Sketchbook 1

Sydney Parkinson

?1745-1771
Born Edinburgh, Scotland

Parkinson was the natural history draughtsman on Captain James Cook's first voyage of circumnavigation. Originally planned as a voyage to Tahiti to observe the Transit of Venus, the scope of the expedition was enlarged into a fully equipped scientific voyage of discovery. This was brought about by Sir Joseph Banks who convinced the Admiralty to allow him and a team of artists and scientists, all at his own expense, to sail with Cook on the *Endeavour.* After observing the transit they went on to discover the eastern coast of Australia and collect and draw the exotic new flora and fauna that they found.

Originally apprenticed to a woollen draper Parkinson went on to teach and practise botanical painting, drawing plants for nurserymen in the London area. After an introduction from the nurseryman James Lee, he was employed by Sir Joseph Banks, at the Botanic Gardens, Kew.

Parkinson sketched plant specimens as they were collected during the field work of the voyage. He would then make these sketches into finished drawings back on board the *Endeavour.* Alternatively he made sufficient notes and partial colouring on the sketch to finish it at a later date.

Sadly, Parkinson died of fever on the return part of the journey and many of his works had to be finished by other artists such as Frederick Polydore Nodder and John Frederick Miller. Parkinson produced 674 sketches and 269 finished watercolours in all and the fig, *Ficus parkinsonii* is named in his honour.

Although 743 copper plates were engraved soon after the drawings were made and are outstanding examples of this craft, they were not printed from until the 1980s. A decade on, Parkinson's drawings have been the inspiration for the Museum's first digital image database.

Thespesia populnea.
Otahiti

Sydney Parkinson pinx 1769.

PARKINSON, Sydney

Thespesia populnea
Indian tulip tree

Watercolour and pencil
476 x 285 mm
1769

MACKENZIE, Daniel
Engraver

Thespesia populnea
Indian tulip tree

Chrome plated copper
465 x 302 mm
ca 1770

PARKINSON, Sydney

Thespesia populnea
Indian tulip tree

Banks Florilegium Print
465 x 302 mm
1987

Keith West

1933 -
Born Buckinghamshire, England

Keith West emigrated to New Zealand in 1950 where he became Botanical Artist for the Botany Division, New Zealand Department of Scientific and Industrial Research from 1959 to 1979. For several years during this period he lectured on art at the University of Canterbury, Christchurch, as well as illustrating many scientific pages and monographs.

In 1976 and 1978 West visited the Missouri Botanical Garden at St. Louis to illustrate North American species of *Epilobia*. He has also worked on commissions for The Natural History Museum.

West returned to Britain in 1980 and now lives in Wales where he continues to work on illustrating books. These include works by Gerald Durrell and Lyall Watson. He is the illustrator for the limited editions of *Songs by George Harrison* and has also written several books on drawing and painting plants. Botanical paintings by West are held in collections around the world.

WEST, Keith

Taraxacum officinale
Dandelion

Acrylic
350 x 332 mm
1982

William MacGillivray

1796-1851
Born Aberdeen, Scotland

Like so many others who were raised in rural surroundings William MacGillivray chose to follow a career in natural history. Ultimately this led him to the Regius Chair of Natural History at Marischal College in Aberdeen in 1841.

MacGillivray was brought up on the island of Lewis, in the Outer Hebrides off the north-west coast of Scotland. The local school had an impressive curriculum and MacGillivray left knowing Latin and Greek as well as the usual subjects taught. He attended the university in Aberdeen and graduated with a general M.A. By his own endeavours and perseverance he gained extensive knowledge of the fauna and flora of the Scottish highlands engaging in field trips where he often walked hundreds of miles. He published on the insects, plants, and birds of the Highlands and at the same time he was employed to curate the Museum of the Royal College of Surgeons in Edinburgh.

By chance he was introduced to the American John James Audubon who was in Edinburgh supervising the production of the plates for his *Birds of America* (1827-1838). Audubon invited MacGillivray to contribute the anatomical and taxonomic sections to his *Ornithological biography*. It seems highly likely that MacGillivray was amazed to see Audubon's life-size paintings and was inspired to make the attempt himself on the British fauna. The result is 213 watercolour paintings of birds, fish, and mammals of the British Isles which rank as some of the most accomplished depictions ever produced. MacGillivray intended to illustrate his five volume *A history of British birds* with coloured plates based on the watercolours but the great expense involved prevented this happening. The watercolours were presented to The Natural History Museum in 1892 by his son P.H. MacGillivray.

MACGILLIVRAY, William

Mustela erminea
Ermine or Stoat, male in winter coat

Watercolour
392 x 525 mm
1834

MACGILLIVRAY,
William

Falco peregrinus
Peregrine falcon

Watercolour
545 x 750 mm
1839

MACGILLIVRAY,
William

Sturnus vulgaris
Starling

Watercolour
262 x 395 mm
ca 1835

MACGILLIVRAY,
William

Zeus faber
John Dory

Watercolour
382 x 561 mm
ca 1835

ZEUS FABER.

II.

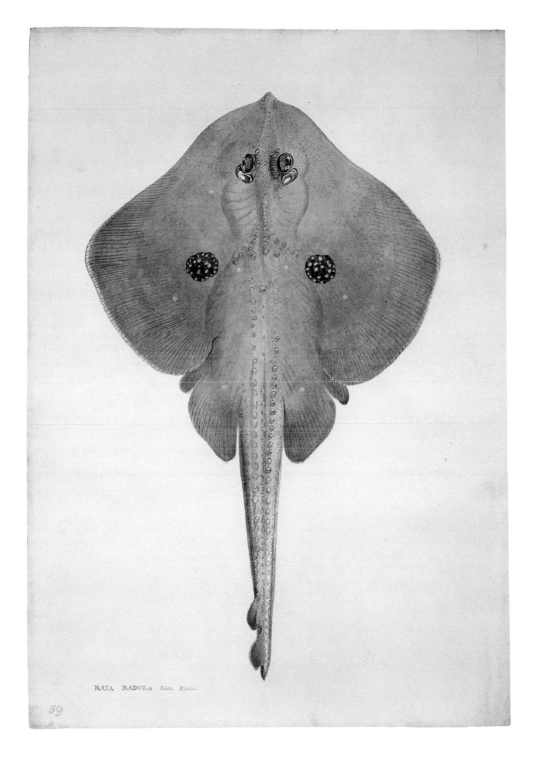

RAJA RADULA Polar. Risso.

MACGILLIVRAY,
William

Raja naevus
Cuckoo ray

Watercolour
558 x 390 mm
ca 1835

MACGILLIVRAY,
William

Ardea cinerea
Grey heron

Watercolour
965 x 735 mm
ca 1835

"Its object is to induce the young to betake themselves,… to the fields and woods, the mountains and shores there to examine for themselves the rich profusion of nature and instead of vaguely admiring the diversified scenery of a district, to be able to mark its individual and minutest features."

William MacGillivray